A B C D E F G

N O P Q R S T U

Meet big **X** and little **x**.

Trace each letter with your finger and say its name.

X is in

fo**x**

X is also in

mi**x**

bo**x**

si**x**

o**x**

Xx Story

Can a fo**x** open a bo**x**
and fi**x** a cake? Yes!

The fo**x** can mi**x** the cake.
The fo**x** can bake the cake.

The fo**x** can put pretty wa**x** candles on top of the cake.

The fo**x** can visit an o**x**
and shout, "SURPRISE!"

Then, the o**x** can say, "Hooray! I am si**x** years old today!"